D1284741

2012

Virginia Maintenance Code

Part III of the Virginia Uniform Statewide Building Code

INTERNATIONAL CODE COUNCIL®

2012 Virginia Maintenance Code

First Printing: March 2014
Second Printing: August 2014

ISBN: 978-1-60983-340-4

COPYRIGHT © 2014
by
International Code Council, Inc.

PRINTED IN THE U.S.A.

PREFACE

Introduction

The *Virginia Uniform Statewide Building Code* (USBC) is a state regulation promulgated by the Virginia Board of Housing and Community Development, a Governor-appointed board, for the purpose of establishing minimum regulations to govern the construction and maintenance of buildings and structures.

The provisions of the USBC are based on nationally recognized model building and fire codes published by the International Code Council, Inc. The model codes are made part of the USBC through a regulatory process known as incorporation by reference. The USBC also contains administrative provisions governing the use of the model codes and establishing requirements for the enforcement of the code by the local building departments and other code enforcement agencies.

In keeping with the designations of the USBC used previously, since the 2012 editions of the *International Codes* are incorporated by reference into this version of the USBC, it is known as the 2012 edition of the USBC.

Arrangement

The USBC is part of the *Virginia Administrative Code* (VAC), the official compilation of state regulations published under the authority and guidance of the Virginia Code Commission. Due to the difference in the section numbering system between the VAC and the model codes incorporated by reference into the USBC, the UBSC utilizes a dual section numbering system. In the USBC, the VAC section numbers are listed first, followed by a section number matching the model code system. In this printing of the USBC, the VAC section numbers are omitted and only the model code numbering system is utilized. The version of the USBC containing both the VAC section numbers and the model code numbering is available from the Virginia Department of Housing and Community Development (DHCD) and may also be accessed through the website of the Virginia Code Commission or by subscription to the VAC.

Overview

The USBC is divided into three stand-alone parts. Part I contains regulations specific to the construction of new buildings and structures and is known as the *Virginia Construction Code*. Part II contains regulations specific to the rehabilitation of existing buildings, including alterations, additions and change of occupancy in existing buildings and structures, and is known as the *Virginia Rehabilitation Code*. Part III of the USBC contains the regulations for the maintenance of existing structures which is enforced at the option of the local governments. It is known as the *Virginia Maintenance Code*.

Codes Purchased from ICC

The 2012 edition of the USBC is being made available in pamphlet form as in past editions of the USBC. In addition to the pamphlet form of the USBC published by DHCD, the International Code Council (ICC) publishes versions of the *Virginia Construction Code, Virginia Rehabilitation Code, Virginia Maintenance Code* and a series of Virginia specific trade codes. In the ICC published versions, marginal markings are provided to distinguish between text that is part of the *International Codes* and text that is part of the state regulations. Double vertical lines in the margins within the body of the codes indicate state amendments to the *International Codes*. As in the standard printings of the *International Codes,* a single vertical line in the margins within the body of the code indicates a technical change from the previous edition of the *International Codes*. Deletions from the previous editions of the *International Codes* are indicated in the form of an arrow (➡) in the margin where an entire section, paragraph, exception or table has been deleted or an item in a list of items or a table has been deleted.

Technical Assistance

The local building departments and enforcing agencies may be contacted for further information concerning the USBC. Contact information for DHCD is below.

DHCD, Division of Building and Fire Regulation
State Building Codes Office
600 East Main Street, Suite 300
Richmond, Virginia 23219
Phone: (804) 371-7150 – Email: sbco@dhcd.virginia.gov
Website: www.dhcd.virginia.gov

TABLE OF CONTENTS

CHAPTER 1

ADMINISTRATION

SECTION 101
GENERAL

101.1 Short title. The *Virginia Uniform Statewide Building Code*, Part III, Maintenance, may be cited as the "*Virginia Maintenance Code*," or as the "VMC."

101.2 Incorporation by reference. Chapters 2–8 of the 2012 *International Property Maintenance Code*, published by the International Code Council, Inc., are adopted and incorporated by reference to be an enforceable part of the VMC. The term "IPMC" means the 2012 *International Property Maintenance Code*, published by the International Code Council, Inc. Any codes and standards referenced in the IPMC are also considered to be part of the incorporation by reference, except that such codes and standards are used only to the prescribed extent of each such reference.

101.3 Numbering system. A dual numbering system is used in the VMC to correlate the numbering system of the *Virginia Administrative Code* with the numbering system of the IPMC. IPMC numbering system designations are provided in the catch-lines of the *Virginia Administrative Code* sections and cross references between sections or chapters of the *Virginia Maintenance Code* use only the IPMC numbering system designations. The term "chapter" is used in the context of the numbering system of the IPMC and may mean a chapter in the VMC, a chapter in the IPMC or a chapter in a referenced code or standard, depending on the context of the use of the term. The term "chapter" is not used to designate a chapter of the *Virginia Administrative Code*, unless clearly indicated.

101.4 Arrangement of code provisions. The VMC is comprised of the combination of (i) the provisions of Chapter 1, Administration, which are established herein, (ii) Chapters 2–8 of the IPMC, which are incorporated by reference in Section 101.2, and (iii) the changes to the text of the incorporated chapters of the IPMC which are specifically identified. The terminology "changes to the text of the incorporated chapters of the IPMC which are specifically identified" shall also be referred to as the "state amendments to the IPMC." Such state amendments to the IPMC are set out using corresponding chapter and section numbers of the IPMC numbering system. In addition, since Chapter 1 of the IPMC is not incorporated as part of the VMC, any reference to a provision of Chapter 1 of the IPMC in the provisions of Chapters 2–8 of the IPMC is generally invalid. However, where the purpose of such a reference would clearly correspond to a provision of Chapter 1 established herein, then the reference may be construed to be a valid reference to such corresponding Chapter 1 provision.

101.5 Use of terminology and notes. The term "this code," or "the code," where used in the provisions of Chapter 1, in Chapters 2–8 of the IPMC, or in the state amendments to the IPMC, means the VMC, unless the context clearly indicates otherwise. The term "this code," or "the code," where used in a code or standard referenced in the IPMC, means that code or standard, unless the context clearly indicates otherwise. The term "USBC" where used in this code means Part I of the USBC, known as the *Virginia Construction Code*, or the VCC, unless the context clearly indicates otherwise. In addition, the use of notes in Chapter 1 is to provide information only and shall not be construed as changing the meaning of any code provision. Notes in the IPMC, in the codes and standards referenced in the IPMC, and in the state amendments to the IPMC, may modify the content of a related provision and shall be considered to be a valid part of the provision, unless the context clearly indicates otherwise.

101.6 Order of precedence. The provisions of this code shall be used as follows:

1. The provisions of Chapter 1 of this code supersede any provisions of Chapters 2–8 of the IPMC that address the same subject matter and impose differing requirements.

2. The provisions of Chapter 1 of this code supersede any provisions of the codes and standards referenced in the IPMC that address the same subject matter and impose differing requirements.

3. The state amendments to the IPMC supersede any provisions of Chapters 2–8 of the IPMC that address the same subject matter and impose differing requirements.

4. The state amendments to the IPMC supersede any provisions of the codes and standards referenced in the IPMC that address the same subject matter and impose differing requirements.

5. The provisions of Chapters 2–8 of the IPMC supersede any provisions of the codes and standards referenced in the IPMC that address the same subject matter and impose differing requirements.

101.7 Administrative provisions. The provisions of Chapter 1 establish administrative requirements, which include but are not limited to provisions relating to the scope of the code, enforcement, fees, permits, inspections and disputes. Any provisions of Chapters 2–8 of the IPMC or any provisions of the codes and standards referenced in the IPMC which address the same subject matter to a lesser or greater extent are deleted and replaced by the provisions of Chapter 1. Further, any administrative requirements contained in the state amendments to the IPMC shall be given the same precedence as the provisions of Chapter 1. Notwithstanding the above, where administrative requirements of Chapters 2–8 of the IPMC or of the codes and standards referenced in the IPMC are specifically identified as valid administrative requirements in Chapter 1 of this code or in the state amendments to the IPMC, then such requirements are not deleted and replaced.

Note: The purpose of this provision is to eliminate overlap, conflicts and duplication by providing a single standard for administrative, procedural and enforcement requirements of this code.

101.8 Definitions. The definitions of terms used in this code are contained in Chapter 2 along with specific provisions addressing the use of definitions. Terms may be defined in other chapters or provisions of the code and such definitions are also valid.

Note: The order of precedence outlined in Section 101.6 may be determinative in establishing how to apply the definitions in the IPMC and in the referenced codes and standards.

SECTION 102
PURPOSE AND SCOPE

102.1 Purpose. In accordance with Section 36-103 of the Code of Virginia, the Virginia Board of Housing and Community Development may adopt and promulgate as part of the *Virginia Uniform Statewide Building Code,* building regulations that facilitate the maintenance, rehabilitation, development and reuse of existing buildings at the least possible cost to ensure the protection of the public health, safety and welfare. Further, in accordance with Section 36-99 of the Code of Virginia, the purpose of this code is to protect the health, safety and welfare of the residents of the Commonwealth of Virginia, provided that buildings and structures should be permitted to be maintained at the least possible cost consistent with recognized standards of health, safety, energy conservation and water conservation, including provisions necessary to prevent overcrowding, rodent or insect infestation, and garbage accumulation; and barrier-free provisions for the physically handicapped and aged.

102.2 Scope. In accordance with Section 36-98 of the Code of Virginia, the VMC shall supersede the building codes and regulations of the counties, municipalities and other political subdivisions and state agencies.

102.3 Exemptions. This code shall not regulate those buildings and structures specifically exempt from the VCC, except that existing industrialized buildings and manufactured homes shall not be exempt from this code.

SECTION 103
APPLICATION OF CODE

103.1 General. This code prescribes regulations for the maintenance of all existing buildings and structures and associated equipment, including regulations for unsafe buildings and structures.

103.2 Maintenance requirements. Buildings and structures shall be maintained and kept in good repair in accordance with the requirements of this code and when applicable in accordance with the USBC under which such building or structure was constructed. No provision of this code shall require alterations to be made to an existing building or structure or to equipment unless conditions are present which meet the definition of an unsafe structure or a structure unfit for human occupancy.

103.2.1 Maintenance of nonrequired fire protection systems. Nonrequired fire protection systems shall be maintained to function as originally installed. If any such

systems are to be reduced in function or discontinued, approval shall be obtained from the building official in accordance with Section 103.8.1 of the VCC.

103.3 Continued approval. Notwithstanding any provision of this code to the contrary, alterations shall not be required to be made to existing buildings or structures which are occupied in accordance with a certificate of occupancy issued under any edition of the USBC.

103.4 Rental inspections. In accordance with Section 36-105.1:1 of the Code of Virginia, these provisions are applicable to rental inspection programs. For purposes of this section:

"**Dwelling unit**" means a building or structure or part thereof that is used for a home or residence by one or more persons who maintain a household.

"**Owner**" means the person shown on the current real estate assessment books or current real estate assessment records.

"**Residential rental dwelling unit**" means a dwelling unit that is leased or rented to one or more tenants. However, a dwelling unit occupied in part by the owner thereof shall not be construed to be a residential rental dwelling unit unless a tenant occupies a part of the dwelling unit that has its own cooking and sleeping areas, and a bathroom, unless otherwise provided in the zoning ordinance by the local governing body.

The local governing body may adopt an ordinance to inspect residential rental dwelling units for compliance with this code and to promote safe, decent and sanitary housing for its citizens, in accordance with the following:

1. Except as provided for in subdivision 3 of this subsection, the dwelling units shall be located in a rental inspection district established by the local governing body in accordance with this section; and

2. The rental inspection district is based upon a finding by the local governing body that (i) there is a need to protect the public health, safety and welfare of the occupants of dwelling units inside the designated rental inspection district; (ii) the residential rental dwelling units within the designated rental inspection district are either (a) blighted or in the process of deteriorating or (b) the residential rental dwelling units are in the need of inspection by the building department to prevent deterioration, taking into account the number, age and condition of residential dwelling rental units inside the proposed rental inspection district; and (iii) the inspection of residential rental dwelling units inside the proposed rental inspection district is necessary to maintain safe, decent and sanitary living conditions for tenants and other residents living in the proposed rental inspection district. Nothing in this section shall be construed to authorize one or more locality-wide rental inspection districts and a local governing body shall limit the boundaries of the proposed rental inspection districts to such areas of the locality that meet the criteria set out in this subsection; or

3. An individual residential rental dwelling unit outside of a designated rental inspection district is made subject to the rental inspection ordinance based upon a separate finding for each individual dwelling unit by the local governing body that (i) there is a need to protect the public health, welfare and safety of the occupants of that individual dwelling unit; (ii) the individual dwelling unit is either (a) blighted or (b) in the process of deteriorating; or (iii) there is evidence of violations of this code that affect the safe, decent and sanitary living conditions for tenants living in such individual dwelling unit.

For purposes of this section, the local governing body may designate a local government agency other than the building department to perform all or part of the duties contained in the enforcement authority granted to the building department by this section.

Before adopting a rental inspection ordinance and establishing a rental inspection district or an amendment to either, the governing body of the locality shall hold a public hearing on the proposed ordinance. Notice of the hearing shall be published once a week for two successive weeks in a newspaper published or having general circulation in the locality.

Upon adoption by the local governing body of a rental inspection ordinance, the building department shall make reasonable efforts to notify owners of residential rental dwelling units in the designated rental inspection district, or their designated managing agents, and to any individual dwelling units subject to the rental inspection ordinance, not located in a rental inspection district, of the adoption of such ordinance, and provide information and an explanation of the rental inspection ordinance and the responsibilities of the owner thereunder.

The rental inspection ordinance may include a provision that requires the owners of dwelling units in a rental inspection district to notify the building department in writing if the dwelling unit of the owner is used for residential rental purposes. The building department may develop a form for such purposes. The rental inspection ordinance shall not include a registration requirement or a fee of any kind associated with the written notification pursuant to this subdivision. A rental inspection ordinance may not require that the written notification from the owner of a dwelling unit subject to a rental inspection ordinance be provided to the building department in less than 60 days after the adoption of a rental inspection ordinance. However, there shall be no penalty for the failure of an owner of a residential rental dwelling unit to comply with the provisions of this subsection, unless and until the building department provides personal or written notice to the property owner, as provided in this section. In any event, the sole penalty for the willful failure of an owner of a dwelling unit who is using the dwelling unit for residential rental purposes to comply with the written notification requirement shall be a civil penalty of up to $50. For purposes of this subsection, notice sent by regular first-class mail to the last known address of the owner as shown on the current real estate tax assessment books or current real estate tax assessment records shall be deemed compliance with this requirement.

Upon establishment of a rental inspection district in accordance with this section, the building department may, in conjunction with the written notifications as provided for above, proceed to inspect dwelling units in the designated rental inspection district to determine if the dwelling units are being used as a residential rental property and for compliance with the provisions of this code that affect the safe, decent and sanitary living conditions for the tenants of such property.

If a multifamily development has more than 10 dwelling units, in the initial and periodic inspections, the building department shall inspect only a sampling of dwelling units, of not less than two and not more than 10 percent of the dwelling units, of a multifamily development, that includes all of the multifamily buildings that are part of that multifamily development. In no event, however, shall the building department charge a fee authorized by this section for inspection of more than 10 dwelling units. If the building department determines upon inspection of the sampling of dwelling units that there are violations of this code that affect the safe, decent and sanitary living conditions for the tenants of such multifamily development, the building department may inspect as many dwelling units as necessary to enforce these provisions, in which case, the fee shall be based upon a charge per dwelling unit inspected, as otherwise provided in the fee schedule established pursuant to this section.

Upon the initial or periodic inspection of a residential rental dwelling unit subject to a rental inspection ordinance, the building department has the authority under these provisions to require the owner of the dwelling unit to submit to such follow-up inspections of the dwelling unit as the building department deems necessary, until such time as the dwelling unit is brought into compliance with the provisions of this code that affect the safe, decent and sanitary living conditions for the tenants.

Except as provided for above, following the initial inspection of a residential rental dwelling unit subject to a rental inspection ordinance, the building department may inspect any residential rental dwelling unit in a rental inspection district, that is not otherwise exempted in accordance with this section, no more than once each calendar year.

Upon the initial or periodic inspection of a residential rental dwelling unit subject to a rental inspection ordinance for compliance with these provisions, provided that there are no violations of this code that affect the safe, decent and sanitary living conditions for the tenants of such residential rental dwelling unit, the building department shall provide, to the owner of such residential rental dwelling unit, an exemption from the rental inspection ordinance for a minimum of four years. Upon the sale of a residential rental dwelling unit, the building department may perform a periodic inspection as provided above, subsequent to such sale. If a residential rental dwelling unit has been issued a certificate of occupancy within the last four years, an exemption shall be granted for a minimum period of four years from the date of the issuance of the certificate of occupancy by the building department. If the residential rental dwelling unit becomes in violation of this code during the exemption period, the building department may revoke the exemption previously granted under this section.

A local governing body may establish a fee schedule for enforcement of these provisions, which includes a per dwelling unit fee for the initial inspections, follow-up inspections and periodic inspections under this section.

The provisions of this section shall not in any way alter the rights and obligations of landlords and tenants pursuant to the applicable provisions of Chapter 13 (Section 55-217 et seq.) or Chapter 13.2 (Section 55-248.2 et seq.) of Title 55 of the Code of Virginia.

The provisions of this section shall not alter the duties or responsibilities of the local building department under Section 36-105 of the Code of Virginia to enforce the USBC.

Unless otherwise provided for in Section 36-105.1:1 of the Code of Virginia, penalties for violation of this section shall be the same as the penalties provided for violations of other sections of the USBC.

SECTION 104
ENFORCEMENT, GENERALLY

104.1 Scope of enforcement. This section establishes the requirements for enforcement of this code in accordance with Section 36-105 of the Code of Virginia. The local governing body may also inspect and enforce the provisions of the USBC for existing buildings and structures, whether occupied or not. Such inspection and enforcement shall be carried out by an agency or department designated by the local governing body.

If the local building department receives a complaint that a violation of this code exists that is an immediate and imminent threat to the health or safety of the owner, tenant, or occupants of any building or structure, or the owner, occupant, or tenant of any nearby building or structure, and the owner, occupant, or tenant of the building or structure that is the subject of the complaint has refused to allow the code official or his agent to have access to the subject building or structure, the code official or his agent may present sworn testimony to a magistrate or court of competent jurisdiction and request that the magistrate or court grant the code official or his agent an inspection warrant to enable the code official or his agent to enter the subject building or structure for the purpose of determining whether violations of this code exist. The code official or his agent shall make a reasonable effort to obtain consent from the owner, occupant, or tenant of the subject building or structure prior to seeking the issuance of an inspection warrant under this section.

Note: Generally, official action must be taken by the local government to enforce the VMC. Consultation with the legal counsel of the jurisdiction when initiating or changing such action is advised.

104.1.1 Transfer of ownership. In accordance with Section 36-105 of the Code of Virginia, if the local building department has initiated an enforcement action against the owner of a building or structure and such owner subsequently transfers the ownership of the building or structure to an entity in which the owner holds an ownership interest greater than 50 percent, the pending enforcement action shall continue to be enforced against the owner.

104.2 Fees. In accordance with Section 36-105 of the Code of Virginia, fees may be levied by the local governing body in order to defray the cost of enforcement and appeals.

104.3 State buildings. In accordance with Section 36-98.1 of the Code of Virginia, this code shall be applicable to state-owned buildings and structures. Acting through the Division of Engineering and Buildings, the Department of General Services shall function as the building official for state-owned buildings.

104.3.1 Certification of state enforcement personnel. State enforcement personnel shall comply with the applicable requirements of Sections 104.4.2 through 104.4.4 for certification, periodic maintenance training, and continuing education.

104.4 Local enforcing agency. In jurisdictions enforcing this code, the local governing body shall designate the agency within the local government responsible for such enforcement and appoint a code official. The local governing body may also utilize technical assistants to assist the code official in the enforcement of this code. A permanently appointed code official shall not be removed from office except for cause after having been afforded a full opportunity to be heard on specific and relevant charges by and before the appointing authority. DHCD shall be notified by the appointing authority within 30 days of the appointment or release of a permanent or acting code official and within 60 days after retaining or terminating a technical assistant.

Note: Code officials and technical assistants are subject to sanctions in accordance with the VCS.

104.4.1 Qualifications of code official and technical assistants. The code official shall have at least five years of building experience as a licensed professional engineer or architect, building, fire or trade inspector, contractor, housing inspector or superintendent of building, fire or trade construction or at least five years of building experience after obtaining a degree in architecture or engineering, with at least three years in responsible charge of work. Any combination of education and experience that would confer equivalent knowledge and ability shall be deemed to satisfy this requirement. The code official shall have general knowledge of sound engineering practice in respect to the design and construction of structures, the basic principles of fire prevention, the accepted requirements for means of egress and the installation of elevators and other service equipment necessary for the health, safety and general welfare of the occupants and the public. The local governing body may establish additional qualification requirements.

A technical assistant shall have at least three years of experience and general knowledge in at least one of the following areas: building construction, building, fire or housing inspections, plumbing, electrical or mechanical trades, fire protection, elevators or property maintenance work. Any combination of education and experience which would confer equivalent knowledge and ability shall be deemed to satisfy this requirement. The locality may establish additional certification requirements.

104.4.2 Certification of code official and technical assistants. An acting or permanent code official shall be certified as a code official in accordance with the VCS within one year after being appointed as acting or permanent code official. A technical assistant shall be certified in the appropriate subject area within 18 months after becoming a technical assistant. When required by a locality to have two or more certifications, a technical assistant shall obtain the additional certifications within three years from the date of such requirement.

> **Exception:** A code official or technical assistant in place prior to April 1, 1995, shall not be required to meet the certification requirements in this section while continuing to serve in the same capacity in the same locality.

104.4.3 Noncertified code official. Except for a code official exempt from certification under the exception to Section 104.4.2, any acting or permanent code official who is not certified as a code official in accordance with the VCS shall attend the core module of the Virginia Building Code Academy or an equivalent course in an individual or regional code academy accredited by DHCD within 180 days of appointment. This requirement is in addition to meeting the certification requirement in Section 104.4.2.

104.4.4 Requirements for periodic maintenance training and education. Code officials and technical assistants shall attend periodic maintenance training as designated by DHCD. In addition to the periodic maintenance training required above, code officials and technical assistants shall attend 16 hours of continuing education every two years as approved by DHCD. If a code official or technical assistant possesses more than one BHCD certificate, the 16 hours shall satisfy the continuing education requirement for all BHCD certificates.

104.4.5 Conflict of interest. The standards of conduct for code officials and technical assistants shall be in accordance with the provisions of the State and Local Government Conflict of Interests Act, Chapter 31 (Section 2.2-3100 et seq.) of Title 2.2 of the Code of Virginia.

104.4.6 Records. The local enforcing agency shall retain a record of applications received, permits, certificates, notices and orders issued, fees collected and reports of inspections in accordance with The Library of Virginia's General Schedule Number Six.

104.5 Powers and duties, generally. The code official shall enforce this code as set out herein and as interpreted by the State Review Board and shall issue all necessary notices or orders to ensure compliance with the code.

104.5.1 Delegation of authority. The code official may delegate powers and duties except where such authority is limited by the local government. When such delegations are made, the code official shall be responsible for assuring that they are carried out in accordance with the provisions of this code.

104.5.2 Issuance of modifications. Upon written application by an owner or an owner's agent, the code official may approve a modification of any provision of this code provided the spirit and intent of the code are observed and public health, welfare and safety are assured. The decision of the code official concerning a modification shall be made in writing and the application for a modification and the decision of the code official concerning such modification shall be retained in the permanent records of the local enforcing agency.

104.5.2.1 Substantiation of modification. The code official may require or may consider a statement from a professional engineer, architect or other person competent in the subject area of the application as to the equivalency of the proposed modification.

104.5.3 Inspections. The code official may inspect buildings or structures to determine compliance with this code and shall carry proper credentials when performing such inspections. The code official is authorized to engage such expert opinion as deemed necessary to report upon unusual, detailed or complex technical issues in accordance with local policies.

104.5.3.1 Observations. When, during an inspection, the code official or authorized representative observes an apparent or actual violation of another law, ordinance, or code not within the official's authority to enforce, such official shall report the findings to the official having jurisdiction in order that such official may institute the necessary measures.

104.5.3.2 Approved inspection agencies and individuals. The code official may accept reports of inspections or tests from individuals or inspection agencies approved in accordance with the code official's written policy required by Section 104.5.3.3. The individual or inspection agency shall meet the qualifications and reliability requirements established by the written policy. Reports of inspections by approved individuals or agencies shall be in writing, shall indicate if compliance with the applicable provisions of this code have been met, and shall be certified by the individual inspector or by the responsible officer when the report is from an agency. The code official shall review and approve the report unless there is cause to reject it. Failure to approve a report shall be in writing within five working days of receiving it, stating the reasons for rejection.

104.5.3.3 Third-party inspectors. Each code official charged with the enforcement of this code and that accepts third-party reports shall have a written policy establishing the minimum acceptable qualifications for third-party inspectors. The policy shall include the format and time frame required for submission of reports, any prequalification or preapproval requirements before conducting a third-party inspection and any other requirements and procedures established by the code official.

104.5.3.4 Qualifications. In determining third-party qualifications, the code official may consider such items as DHCD inspector certification, other state or national certifications, state professional registrations, related experience, education, and any other factors that would demonstrate competency and reliability to conduct inspections.

104.5.4 Notices, reports and orders. Upon findings by the code official that violations of this code exist, the code official shall issue a correction notice or notice of violation to the owner or the person responsible for the maintenance of the structure. Work done to correct violations of this code subject to the permit, inspection and approval provisions of the VCC shall not be construed as authorization to extend the time limits established for compliance with this code.

104.5.4.1 Correction notice. The correction notice shall be a written notice of the defective conditions. The correction notice shall require correction of the violation or violations within a reasonable time unless an emergency condition exists as provided under the unsafe building provisions of Section 105. Upon request, the correction notice shall reference the code section that serves as the basis for the defects and shall state that such defects shall be corrected and reinspected in a reasonable time designated by the code official.

104.5.4.2 Notice of violation. If the code official determines there are violations of this code other than those for unsafe structures, unsafe equipment or structures unfit for human occupancy under Section 105, the code official may issue a notice of violation to be communicated promptly in writing to the owner or the person responsible for the maintenance or use of the building or structure in lieu of a correction notice as provided for in Section 104.5.4.1. In addition, the code official shall issue a notice of violation for any uncorrected violation remaining from a correction notice established in Section 104.5.4.1. A notice of violation shall be issued by the code official before initiating legal proceedings unless the conditions violate the unsafe building conditions of Section 105 and the provisions established therein are followed. The code official shall provide the section numbers to the owner for any code provision cited in the notice of violation. The notice shall require correction of the violation or violations within a reasonable time unless an emergency condition exists as provided under the building provisions of Section 105. The owner or person to whom the notice of violation has been issued shall be responsible for contacting the code official within the time frame established for any reinspections to assure the violations have been corrected. The code official will be responsible for making such inspection and verifying the violations have been corrected. In addition, the notice of violation shall indicate the right of appeal by referencing the appeals section of this code.

104.5.5 Coordination of inspections. The code official shall coordinate inspections and administrative orders with any other state or local agencies having related inspection authority and shall coordinate those inspections required by the *Virginia Statewide Fire Prevention Code* (13VAC5-51) for maintenance of fire protection devices, equipment and assemblies so that the owners and occu-

pants will not be subjected to numerous inspections or conflicting orders.

Note: The *Fire Prevention Code* requires the fire official to coordinate such inspections with the code official.

104.5.6 Further action when violation not corrected. If the responsible party has not complied with the notice of violation, the code official shall submit a written request to the legal counsel of the locality to institute the appropriate legal proceedings to restrain, correct or abate the violation or to require the removal or termination of the use of the building or structure involved. In cases where the locality so authorizes, the code official may issue or obtain a summons or warrant.

104.5.7 Penalties and abatement. Penalties for violations of this code shall be as set out in Section 36-106 of the Code of Virginia. The successful prosecution of a violation of the code shall not preclude the institution of appropriate legal action to require correction or abatement of a violation.

SECTION 105
UNSAFE STRUCTURES OR STRUCTURES UNFIT FOR HUMAN OCCUPANCY

105.1 General. This section shall apply to existing structures which are classified as unsafe or unfit for human occupancy. All conditions causing such structures to be classified as unsafe or unfit for human occupancy shall be remedied or as an alternative to correcting such conditions, the structure may be vacated and secured against public entry or razed and removed. Vacant and secured structures shall still be subject to other applicable requirements of this code. Notwithstanding the above, when the code official determines that an unsafe structure or a structure unfit for human occupancy constitutes such a hazard that it should be razed or removed, then the code official shall be permitted to order the demolition of such structures in accordance with applicable requirements of this code.

Note: Structures which become unsafe during construction are regulated under the VCC.

105.2 Inspection of unsafe or unfit structures. The code official shall inspect any structure reported or discovered as unsafe or unfit for human habitation and shall prepare a report to be filed in the records of the local enforcing agency and a copy issued to the owner. The report shall include the use of the structure and a description of the nature and extent of any conditions found.

105.3 Unsafe conditions not related to maintenance. When the code official finds a condition that constitutes a serious and dangerous hazard to life or health in a structure constructed prior to the initial edition of the USBC and when that condition is of a cause other than improper maintenance or failure to comply with state or local building codes that were in effect when the structure was constructed, then the code official shall be permitted to order those minimum changes to the design or construction of the structure to remedy the condition.

105.3.1 Limitation to requirements for retrofitting. In accordance with Section 103.2, this code does not generally provide for requiring the retrofitting of any structure. However, conditions may exist in structures constructed prior to the initial edition of the USBC because of faulty design or equipment that constitute a danger to life or health or a serious hazard. Any changes to the design or construction required by the code official under this section shall be only to remedy the serious hazard or danger to life or health and such changes shall not be required to fully comply with the requirements of the VCC applicable to newly constructed buildings or structures.

105.4 Notice of unsafe structure or structure unfit for human occupancy. When a structure is determined to be unsafe or unfit for human occupancy by the code official, a written notice of unsafe structure or structure unfit for human occupancy shall be issued by personal service to the owner, the owner's agent or the person in control of such structure. The notice shall specify the corrections necessary to comply with this code, or if the structure is required to be demolished, the notice shall specify the time period within which the demolition must occur. Requirements in Section 104.5.4 for notices of violation are also applicable to notices issued under this section to the extent that any such requirements are not in conflict with the requirements of this section.

Note: Whenever possible, the notice should also be given to any tenants of the affected structure.

105.4.1 Vacating unsafe structure. If the code official determines there is actual and immediate danger to the occupants or public, or when life is endangered by the occupancy of an unsafe structure, the code official shall be authorized to order the occupants to immediately vacate the unsafe structure. When an unsafe structure is ordered to be vacated, the code official shall post a notice with the following wording at each entrance: "THIS STRUCTURE IS UNSAFE AND ITS OCCUPANCY (OR USE) IS PROHIBITED BY THE CODE OFFICIAL." After posting, occupancy or use of the unsafe structure shall be prohibited except when authorized to enter to conduct inspections, make required repairs or as necessary to demolish the structure.

105.5 Posting of notice. If the notice is unable to be issued by personal service as required by Section 105.4, then the notice shall be sent by registered or certified mail to the last known address of the responsible party and a copy of the notice shall be posted in a conspicuous place on the premises.

105.6 Posting of placard. In the case of a structure unfit for human habitation, at the time the notice is issued, a placard with the following wording shall be posted at the entrance to the structure: "THIS STRUCTURE IS UNFIT FOR HABITATION AND ITS USE OR OCCUPANCY HAS BEEN PROHIBITED BY THE CODE OFFICIAL." In the case of an unsafe structure, if the notice is not complied with, a placard with the above wording shall be posted at the entrance to the structure. After a structure is placarded, entering the structure shall be prohibited except as authorized by the code official to make inspections, to perform required repairs or to demolish the structure. In addition, the placard shall not be removed until the structure is determined by the code official to be safe to occupy, nor shall the placard be defaced.

105.7 Revocation of certificate of occupancy. If a notice of unsafe structure or structure unfit for human habitation is not complied with within the time period stipulated on the notice, the code official shall be permitted to request the local building department to revoke the certificate of occupancy issued under the VCC.

105.8 Vacant and open structures. When an unsafe structure or a structure unfit for human habitation is open for public entry at the time a placard is issued under Section 105.6, the code official shall be permitted to authorize the necessary work to make such structure secure against public entry whether or not legal action to compel compliance has been instituted.

105.9 Emergency repairs and demolition. To the extent permitted by the locality, the code official may authorize emergency repairs to unsafe structures or structures unfit for human habitation when it is determined that there is an immediate danger of any portion of the unsafe structure or structure unfit for human habitation collapsing or falling and when life is endangered. Emergency repairs may also be authorized where there is a code violation resulting in the immediate serious and imminent threat to the life and safety of the occupants. The code official shall be permitted to authorize the necessary work to make the structure temporarily safe whether or not legal action to compel compliance has been instituted. In addition, whenever an owner of an unsafe structure or structure unfit for human habitation fails to comply with a notice to demolish issued under Section 105.4 in the time period stipulated, the code official shall be permitted to cause the structure to be demolished. In accordance with Sections 15.2-906 and 15.2-1115 of the Code of Virginia, the legal counsel of the locality may be requested to institute appropriate action against the property owner to recover the costs associated with any such emergency repairs or demolition and every such charge that remains unpaid shall constitute a lien against the property on which the emergency repairs or demolition were made and shall be enforceable in the same manner as provided in Articles 3 (Section 58.1-3490 et seq.) and 4 (Section 58.1-3965 et seq.) of Chapter 39 of Title 58.1 of the Code of Virginia.

Note: Code officials and local governing bodies should be aware that other statutes and court decisions may impact on matters relating to demolition, in particular whether newspaper publication is required if the owner cannot be located and whether the demolition order must be delayed until the owner has been given the opportunity for a hearing. In addition, historic building demolition may be prevented by authority granted to local historic review boards in accordance with Section 15.2-2306 of the Code of Virginia unless determined necessary by the code official.

105.10 Closing of streets. When necessary for public safety, the code official shall be permitted to order the temporary closing of sidewalks, streets, public ways or premises adjacent to unsafe or unfit structures and prohibit the use of such spaces.

SECTION 106
APPEALS

106.1 Establishment of appeals board. In accordance with Section 36-105 of the Code of Virginia, there shall be established within each local enforcing agency a Local Board of Building Code Appeals (LBBCA). Whenever a county or a municipality does not have such a LBBCA, the local governing body shall enter into an agreement with the local governing body of another county or municipality or with some other agency, or a state agency approved by DHCD for such appeals resulting therefrom. Fees may be levied by the local governing body in order to defray the cost of such appeals. The LBBCA for hearing appeals under the VCC shall be permitted to serve as the appeals board required by this section. The locality is responsible for maintaining a duly constituted LBBCA prepared to hear appeals within the time limits established in this section. The LBBCA shall meet as necessary to assure a duly constituted board, appoint officers as necessary, and receive such training on the code as may be appropriate or necessary from staff of the locality.

106.2 Membership of board. The LBBCA shall consist of at least five members appointed by the locality for a specific term of office established by written policy. Alternate members may be appointed to serve in the absence of any regular members and as such, shall have the full power and authority of the regular members. Regular and alternate members may be reappointed. Written records of current membership, including a record of the current chairman and secretary shall be maintained in the office of the locality. In order to provide continuity, the terms of the members may be of different length so that less than half will expire in any one-year period.

106.3 Officers and qualifications of members. The LBBCA shall annually select one of its regular members to serve as chairman. When the chairman is not present at an appeal hearing, the members present shall select an acting chairman. The locality or the chief executive officer of the locality shall appoint a secretary to the LBBCA to maintain a detailed record of all proceedings. Members of the LBBCA shall be selected by the locality on the basis of their ability to render fair and competent decisions regarding application of the USBC and shall to the extent possible, represent different occupational or professional fields relating to the construction industry. At least one member should be an experienced builder; at least one member should be an RDP, and at least one member should be an experienced property manager. Employees or officials of the locality shall not serve as members of the LBBCA.

106.4 Conduct of members. No member shall hear an appeal in which that member has a conflict of interest in accordance with the State and Local Government Conflict of Interests Act (Section 2.2-3100 et seq. of the Code of Virginia). Members shall not discuss the substance of an appeal with any other party or their representatives prior to any hearings.

106.5 Right of appeal; filing of appeal application. Any person aggrieved by the local enforcing agency's application of this code or the refusal to grant a modification to the provisions of this code may appeal to the LBBCA. The applicant shall submit a written request for appeal to the LBBCA within 14 calendar days of the receipt of the decision being appealed. The application shall contain the name and address of the owner of the building or structure and, in addition, the name and address of the person appealing, when the applicant is not the owner. A copy of the code official's decision shall be submitted along with the application for appeal and maintained as part of the record. The application shall be marked by the LBBCA to indicate the date received. Failure to submit an application for appeal within the time limit established by this section shall constitute acceptance of a code official's decision.

106.6 Meetings and postponements. The LBBCA shall meet within 30 calendar days after the date of receipt of the application for appeal, except that a period of up to 45 calendar days shall be permitted where the LBBCA has regularly scheduled monthly meetings. A longer time period shall be permitted if agreed to by all the parties involved in the appeal. A notice indicating the time and place of the hearing shall be sent to the parties in writing to the addresses listed on the application at least 14 calendar days prior to the date of the hearing, except that a lesser time period shall be permitted if agreed to by all the parties involved in the appeal. When a quorum of the LBBCA is not present at a hearing to hear an appeal, any party involved in the appeal shall have the right to request a postponement of the hearing. The LBBCA shall reschedule the appeal within 30 calendar days of the postponement, except that a longer time period shall be permitted if agreed to by all the parties involved in the appeal.

106.7 Hearings and decision. All hearings before the LBBCA shall be open meetings and the appellant, the appellant's representative, the locality's representative and any person whose interests are affected by the code official's decision in question shall be given an opportunity to be heard. The chairman shall have the power and duty to direct the hearing, rule upon the acceptance of evidence and oversee the record of all proceedings. The LBBCA shall have the power to uphold, reverse or modify the decision of the official by a concurring vote of a majority of those present. Decisions of the LBBCA shall be final if no further appeal is made. The decision of the LBBCA shall be by resolution signed by the chairman and retained as part of the record of the appeal. Copies of the resolution shall be sent to all parties by certified mail. In addition, the resolution shall contain the following wording:

"Any person who was a party to the appeal may appeal to the State Review Board by submitting an application to such Board within 21 calendar days upon receipt by certified mail of this resolution. Application forms are available from the Office of the State Review Board, 600 East Main Street, Richmond, Virginia 23219, (804) 371-7150."

106.8 Appeals to the State Review Board. After final determination by the LBBCA in an appeal, any person who was a party to the appeal may further appeal to the State Review Board. In accordance with Section 36-98.2 of the Code of Virginia for state-owned buildings and structures, appeals by an involved state agency from the decision of the code official for state-owned buildings or structures shall be made directly to the State Review Board. The application for appeal shall be made to the State Review Board within 21 calendar days of the receipt of the decision to be appealed. Failure to submit an application within that time limit shall constitute an acceptance of the code official's decision. For appeals from a LBBCA, a copy of the code official's decision and the resolution of the LBBCA shall be submitted with the application for appeal to the State Review Board. Upon request by the Office of the State Review Board, the LBBCA shall submit a copy of all pertinent information from the record of the appeal. In the case of appeals involving state-owned buildings or structures, the involved state agency shall submit a copy of the code official's decision and other relevant information with the application for appeal to the State Review Board. Procedures of the State Review Board are in accordance with Article 2 (Section 36-108 et seq.) of Chapter 6 of Title 36 of the Code of Virginia. Decisions of the State Review Board shall be final if no further appeal is made.

CHAPTER 2

DEFINITIONS

SECTION 201
GENERAL

201.1 Scope. Unless otherwise expressly stated, the following terms shall, for the purposes of this code, have the meanings shown in this chapter.

201.2 Interchangeability. Words stated in the present tense include the future; words stated in the masculine gender include the feminine and neuter; the singular number includes the plural and the plural, the singular.

201.3 Terms defined in other codes. Where terms are not defined in this code and are defined in the *International Building Code, International Fire Code, International Fuel Gas Code, International Plumbing Code, International Mechanical Code, International Existing Building Code, International Residential Code, International Zoning Code* or NFPA 70, such terms shall have the meanings ascribed to them as stated in those codes, except that terms defined in the VCC shall be used for this code and shall take precedence over other definitions.

201.4 Terms not defined. Where terms are not defined through the methods authorized by this section, such terms shall have ordinarily accepted meanings such as the context implies.

201.5 Parts. Whenever the words "*dwelling unit,*" "dwelling," "*premises,*" "building," "*rooming house,*" "*rooming unit,*" "*housekeeping unit*" or "story" are stated in this code, they shall be construed as though they were followed by the words "or any part thereof."

SECTION 202
GENERAL DEFINITIONS

ANCHORED. Secured in a manner that provides positive connection.

[A] APPROVED. *Approved* by the *code official.*

BASEMENT. That portion of a building which is partly or completely below grade.

BATHROOM. A room containing plumbing fixtures including a bathtub or shower.

BEDROOM. Any room or space used or intended to be used for sleeping purposes in either a dwelling or *sleeping unit.*

[A] CODE OFFICIAL. The official who is charged with the administration and enforcement of this code, or any duly authorized representative.

CONDEMN. To adjudge unfit for *occupancy.*

DETACHED. When a structural element is physically disconnected from another and that connection is necessary to provide a positive connection.

DETERIORATION. To weaken, disintegrate, corrode, rust or decay and lose effectiveness.

[B] DWELLING UNIT. A single unit providing complete, independent living facilities for one or more persons, including permanent provisions for living, sleeping, eating, cooking and sanitation.

[Z] EASEMENT. That portion of land or property reserved for present or future use by a person or agency other than the legal fee *owner*(s) of the property. The *easement* shall be permitted to be for use under, on or above a said lot or lots.

EQUIPMENT SUPPORT. Those structural members or assemblies of members or manufactured elements, including braces, frames, lugs, snuggers, hangers or saddles, that transmit gravity load, lateral load and operating load between the equipment and the structure.

EXTERIOR PROPERTY. The open space on the *premises* and on adjoining property under the control of *owners* or *operators* of such *premises.*

GARBAGE. The animal or vegetable waste resulting from the handling, preparation, cooking and consumption of food.

[B] GUARD. A building component or a system of building components located at or near the open sides of elevated walking surfaces that minimizes the possibility of a fall from the walking surface to a lower level.

[B] HABITABLE SPACE. Space in a structure for living, sleeping, eating or cooking. *Bathrooms, toilet rooms,* closets, halls, storage or utility spaces, and similar areas are not considered *habitable spaces.*

HOUSEKEEPING UNIT. A room or group of rooms forming a single *habitable space* equipped and intended to be used for living, sleeping, cooking and eating which does not contain, within such a unit, a toilet, lavatory and bathtub or shower.

IMMINENT DANGER. A condition which could cause serious or life-threatening injury or death at any time.

INFESTATION. The presence, within or contiguous to, a structure or *premises* of insects, rats, vermin or other pests.

INOPERABLE MOTOR VEHICLE. A vehicle which cannot be driven upon the public streets for reason including but not limited to being unlicensed, wrecked, abandoned, in a state of disrepair, or incapable of being moved under its own power.

[A] LABELED. Equipment, materials or products to which have been affixed a label, seal, symbol or other identifying mark of a nationally recognized testing laboratory, inspection agency or other organization concerned with product evaluation that maintains periodic inspection of the production of the above-*labeled* items and whose labeling indicates either that the equipment, material or product meets identified standards or has been tested and found suitable for a specified purpose.

LET FOR OCCUPANCY or LET. To permit, provide or offer possession or *occupancy* of a dwelling, *dwelling unit*, *rooming unit*, building, premise or structure by a person who is or is not the legal *owner* of record thereof, pursuant to a written or unwritten lease, agreement or license, or pursuant to a recorded or unrecorded agreement of contract for the sale of land.

NEGLECT. The lack of proper maintenance for a building or *structure*.

[A] OCCUPANCY. The purpose for which a building or portion thereof is utilized or occupied.

OCCUPANT. Any individual living or sleeping in a building, or having possession of a space within a building.

OPENABLE AREA. That part of a window, skylight or door which is available for unobstructed *ventilation* and which opens directly to the outdoors.

OPERATOR. Any person who has charge, care or control of a structure or *premises* which is let or offered for *occupancy*.

[A] OWNER. Any person, agent, *operator*, firm or corporation having a legal or equitable interest in the property; or recorded in the official records of the state, county or municipality as holding title to the property; or otherwise having control of the property, including the guardian of the estate of any such person, and the executor or administrator of the estate of such person if ordered to take possession of real property by a court.

PERSON. An individual, corporation, partnership or any other group acting as a unit.

PEST ELIMINATION. The control and elimination of insects, rodents or other pests by eliminating their harborage places; by removing or making inaccessible materials that serve as their food or water; by other *approved pest elimination* methods.

[A] PREMISES. A lot, plot or parcel of land, *easement* or *public way*, including any structures thereon.

[A] PUBLIC WAY. Any street, alley or similar parcel of land essentially unobstructed from the ground to the sky, which is deeded, dedicated or otherwise permanently appropriated to the public for public use.

ROOMING HOUSE. A building arranged or occupied for lodging, with or without meals, for compensation and not occupied as a one- or two-family dwelling.

ROOMING UNIT. Any room or group of rooms forming a single habitable unit occupied or intended to be occupied for sleeping or living, but not for cooking purposes.

RUBBISH. Combustible and noncombustible waste materials, except garbage; the term shall include the residue from the burning of wood, coal, coke and other combustible materials, paper, rags, cartons, boxes, wood, excelsior, rubber, leather, tree branches, *yard* trimmings, tin cans, metals, mineral matter, glass, crockery and dust and other similar materials.

[B] SLEEPING UNIT. A room or space in which people sleep, which can also include permanent provisions for living, eating and either sanitation or kitchen facilities, but not both. Such rooms and spaces that are also part of a *dwelling unit* are not *sleeping units*.

STRICT LIABILITY OFFENSE. An offense in which the prosecution in a legal proceeding is not required to prove criminal intent as a part of its case. It is enough to prove that the defendant either did an act which was prohibited, or failed to do an act which the defendant was legally required to do.

[A] STRUCTURE. That which is built or constructed or a portion thereof.

STRUCTURE UNFIT FOR HUMAN OCCUPANCY. An existing structure determined by the code official to be dangerous to the health, safety and welfare of the occupants of the structure or the public because (i) of the degree to which the structure is in disrepair or lacks maintenance, ventilation, illumination, sanitary or heating facilities or other essential equipment, or (ii) the required plumbing and sanitary facilities are inoperable.

TENANT. A person, corporation, partnership or group, whether or not the legal *owner* of record, occupying a building or portion thereof as a unit.

TOILET ROOM. A room containing a water closet or urinal but not a bathtub or shower.

ULTIMATE DEFORMATION. The deformation at which failure occurs and which shall be deemed to occur if the sustainable load reduces to 80 percent or less of the maximum strength.

UNSAFE EQUIPMENT. Unsafe equipment includes any boiler, heating equipment, elevator, moving stairway, electrical wiring or device, flammable liquid containers or other equipment that is in such disrepair or condition that such equipment is determined by the code official to be dangerous to the health, safety and welfare of the occupants of a structure or the public.

UNSAFE STRUCTURE. An existing structure (i) determined by the code official to be dangerous to the health, safety and welfare of the occupants of the structure or the public, (ii) that contains unsafe equipment, or (iii) that is so damaged, decayed, dilapidated, structurally unsafe or of such faulty construction or unstable foundation that partial or complete collapse is likely. A vacant existing structure unsecured or open shall be deemed to be an unsafe structure.

[M] VENTILATION. The natural or mechanical process of supplying conditioned or unconditioned air to, or removing such air from, any space.

WORKMANLIKE. Executed in a skilled manner; e.g., generally plumb, level, square, in line, undamaged and without marring adjacent work.

[Z] YARD. An open space on the same lot with a structure.

CHAPTER 3
GENERAL REQUIREMENTS

SECTION 301
GENERAL

301.1 Scope. The provisions of this chapter shall govern the minimum conditions and the responsibilities of persons for maintenance of structures, equipment and *exterior property*.

301.2 Responsibility. The *owner* of the *premises* shall maintain the structures and *exterior property* in compliance with these requirements, except as otherwise provided for in this code. A person shall not occupy as owner-occupant or permit another person to occupy *premises* which are not in a sanitary and safe condition and which do not comply with the requirements of this chapter. *Occupants* of a *dwelling unit, rooming unit* or *housekeeping unit* are responsible for keeping in a clean, sanitary and safe condition that part of the *dwelling unit, rooming unit, housekeeping unit* or *premises* which they occupy and control.

301.3 Vacant structures and land. All vacant structures and *premises* thereof or vacant land shall be maintained in a clean, safe, secure and sanitary condition as provided herein so as not to cause a blighting problem or adversely affect the public health or safety.

SECTION 302
EXTERIOR PROPERTY AREAS

302.1 Sanitation. (Section deleted)

302.2 Grading and drainage. All premises shall be graded and maintained to protect the foundation walls or slab of the structure from the accumulation and drainage of surface or stagnant water in accordance with the VCC.

302.3 Sidewalks and driveways. All sidewalks, walkways, stairs, driveways, parking spaces and similar spaces regulated under the VCC shall be kept in a proper state of repair, and maintained free from hazardous conditions. Stairs shall comply with the requirements of Sections 305 and 702.

302.4 Weeds. (Section deleted)

302.5 Rodent harborage. All structures and adjacent premises shall be kept free from rodent harborage and infestation where such harborage or infestation adversely affects the structures.

302.6 Exhaust vents. Pipes, ducts, conductors, fans or blowers shall not discharge gases, steam, vapor, hot air, grease, smoke, odors or other gaseous or particulate wastes directly upon abutting or adjacent public or private property or that of another *tenant*.

302.7 Accessory structures. All accessory structures, including *detached* garages, fences and walls, shall be maintained structurally sound and in good repair.

302.8 Motor vehicles. (Section deleted)

302.9 Defacement of property. (Section deleted)

SECTION 303
SWIMMING POOLS, SPAS AND HOT TUBS

303.1 Swimming pools. Swimming pools shall be maintained in a clean and sanitary condition, and in good repair.

303.2 Enclosures. Private swimming pools, hot tubs and spas, containing water more than 24 inches (610 mm) in depth shall be completely surrounded by a fence or barrier at least 48 inches (1219 mm) in height above the finished ground level measured on the side of the barrier away from the pool. Gates and doors in such barriers shall be self-closing and self-latching. Where the self-latching device is a minimum of 54 inches (1372 mm) above the bottom of the gate, the release mechanism shall be located on the pool side of the gate. Self-closing and self-latching gates shall be maintained such that the gate will positively close and latch when released from an open position of 6 inches (152 mm) from the gatepost. No existing pool enclosure shall be removed, replaced or changed in a manner that reduces its effectiveness as a safety barrier.

> **Exception:** Spas or hot tubs with a safety cover that complies with ASTM F 1346 shall be exempt from the provisions of this section.

SECTION 304
EXTERIOR STRUCTURE

304.1 General. The exterior of a structure shall be maintained in good repair, structurally sound and sanitary so as not to pose a threat to the public health, safety or welfare.

304.1.1 Unsafe conditions. (Section deleted)

304.2 Protective treatment. All exterior surfaces, including but not limited to, doors, door and window frames, cornices, porches, trim, balconies, decks and fences, shall be maintained in good condition. Exterior wood surfaces, other than decay-resistant woods, shall be protected from the elements and decay by painting or other protective covering or treatment. Peeling, flaking and chipped paint shall be eliminated and surfaces repainted. All siding and masonry joints, as well as those between the building envelope and the perimeter of windows, doors and skylights, shall be maintained weather resistant and water tight. All metal surfaces subject to rust or corrosion shall be coated to inhibit such rust and corrosion, and all surfaces with rust or corrosion shall be stabilized and coated to inhibit future rust and corrosion. Oxidation stains shall be removed from exterior surfaces. Surfaces designed for stabilization by oxidation are exempt from this requirement.

[F] 304.3 Premises identification. Buildings shall have *approved* address numbers placed in a position to be plainly legible and visible from the street or road fronting the property. These numbers shall contrast with their background. Address numbers shall be Arabic numerals or alphabet letters. Numbers shall be a minimum of 4 inches (102 mm) in height with a minimum stroke width of 0.5 inch (12.7 mm).

304.4 Structural members. All structural members shall be maintained free from *deterioration*, and shall be capable of safely supporting the imposed dead and live loads.

304.5 Foundation walls. All foundation walls shall be maintained plumb and free from open cracks and breaks and shall be kept in such condition so as to prevent the entry of rodents and other pests.

304.6 Exterior walls. All exterior walls shall be free from holes, breaks, and loose or rotting materials; and maintained weatherproof and properly surface coated where required to prevent *deterioration*.

304.7 Roofs and drainage. The roof and flashing shall be sound, tight and not have defects that admit rain. Roof drainage shall be adequate to prevent dampness or deterioration in the walls or interior portion of the structure. Roof drains, gutters and downspouts shall be maintained in good repair and free from obstructions. Roof water shall be discharged in a manner to protect the foundation or slab of buildings and structures from the accumulation of roof drainage.

304.8 Decorative features. All cornices, belt courses, corbels, terra cotta trim, wall facings and similar decorative features shall be maintained in good repair with proper anchorage and in a safe condition.

304.9 Overhang extensions. All overhang extensions including, but not limited to canopies, marquees, signs, metal awnings, fire escapes, standpipes and exhaust ducts shall be maintained in good repair and be properly *anchored* so as to be kept in a sound condition. When required, all exposed surfaces of metal or wood shall be protected from the elements and against decay or rust by periodic application of weather-coating materials, such as paint or similar surface treatment.

304.10 Stairways, decks, porches and balconies. Every exterior stairway, deck, porch and balcony, and all appurtenances attached thereto, shall be maintained structurally sound, in good repair, with proper anchorage and capable of supporting the imposed loads.

304.11 Chimneys and towers. All chimneys, cooling towers, smoke stacks, and similar appurtenances shall be maintained structurally safe and sound, and in good repair. All exposed surfaces of metal or wood shall be protected from the elements and against decay or rust by periodic application of weather-coating materials, such as paint or similar surface treatment.

304.12 Handrails and guards. Every handrail and *guard* shall be firmly fastened and capable of supporting normally imposed loads and shall be maintained in good condition.

304.13 Window, skylight and door frames. Every window, skylight, door and frame shall be kept in sound condition, good repair and weather tight.

304.13.1 Glazing. All glazing materials shall be maintained free from cracks and holes.

304.13.2 Openable windows. Every window, other than a fixed window, shall be easily openable and capable of being held in position by window hardware.

304.14 Insect screens. During the period from April 1 to December 1, every door, window and other outside opening required for ventilation of habitable rooms, food preparation areas, food service areas or any areas where products to be included or utilized in food for human consumption are processed, manufactured, packaged or stored, shall be supplied with approved tightly fitting screens of not less than 16 mesh per inch (16 mesh per 25 mm) and every screen door used for insect control shall have a self-closing device in good working condition.

Exception: Screens shall not be required where other approved means, such as mechanical ventilation, air curtains or insect repellant fans, are used.

304.15 Doors. All exterior doors, door assemblies, operator systems if provided, and hardware shall be maintained in good condition. Locks at all entrances to dwelling units and sleeping units shall tightly secure the door. Locks on means of egress doors shall be in accordance with Section 702.3.

304.16 Basement hatchways. Every *basement* hatchway shall be maintained to prevent the entrance of rodents, rain and surface drainage water.

304.17 Guards for basement windows. Every *basement* window that is openable shall be supplied with rodent shields, storm windows or other *approved* protection against the entry of rodents.

304.18 Building security. (Section deleted)

304.18.1 Doors. (Section deleted)

304.18.2 Windows. (Section deleted)

304.18.3 Basement hatchways. (Section deleted)

304.19 Gates. All exterior gates, gate assemblies, operator systems if provided, and hardware shall be maintained in good condition. Latches at all entrances shall tightly secure the gates.

SECTION 305
INTERIOR STRUCTURE

305.1 General. The interior of a structure and equipment therein shall be maintained in good repair, structurally sound and in a sanitary condition. *Occupants* shall keep that part of the structure which they occupy or control in a clean and sanitary condition. Every *owner* of a structure containing a *rooming house*, *housekeeping units*, a hotel, a dormitory, two or more *dwelling unit*s or two or more nonresidential occupancies, shall maintain, in a clean and sanitary condition, the shared or public areas of the structure and *exterior property*.

305.1.1 Unsafe conditions. (Section deleted)

305.2 Structural members. All structural members shall be maintained structurally sound, and be capable of supporting the imposed loads.

305.3 Interior surfaces. All interior surfaces, including windows and doors, shall be maintained in good, clean and sanitary condition. Peeling, chipping, flaking or abraded paint shall be repaired, removed or covered. Cracked or loose plaster, decayed wood and other defective surface conditions shall be corrected.

305.4 Stairs and walking surfaces. Every stair, ramp, landing, balcony, porch, deck or other walking surface shall be maintained in sound condition and good repair.

305.5 Handrails and guards. Every handrail and *guard* shall be firmly fastened and capable of supporting normally imposed loads and shall be maintained in good condition.

305.6 Interior doors. Every interior door shall fit reasonably well within its frame and shall be capable of being opened and closed by being properly and securely attached to jambs, headers or tracks as intended by the manufacturer of the attachment hardware.

305.7 Carbon monoxide alarms. Carbon monoxide alarms shall be maintained as approved.

SECTION 306
COMPONENT SERVICEABILITY
(Section deleted in its entirety)

SECTION 307
HANDRAILS AND GUARDRAILS

307.1 General. Every exterior and interior flight of stairs having more than four risers shall have a handrail on one side of the stair and every open portion of a stair, landing, balcony, porch, deck, ramp or other walking surface which is more than 30 inches (762 mm) above the floor or grade below shall have *guards*. Handrails shall not be less than 30 inches (762 mm) in height or more than 42 inches (1067 mm) in height measured vertically above the nosing of the tread or above the finished floor of the landing or walking surfaces. *Guards* shall not be less than 30 inches (762 mm) in height above the floor of the landing, balcony, porch, deck, or ramp or other walking surface.

Exception: *Guards* shall not be required where exempted by the adopted building code.

SECTION 308
RUBBISH AND GARBAGE

308.1 Accumulation of rubbish and garbage. The interior of every structure shall be free from excessive accumulation of rubbish or garbage.

308.2 Disposal of rubbish. (Section deleted)

308.2.1 Rubbish storage facilities. (Section deleted)

308.2.2 Refrigerators. (Section deleted)

308.3 Disposal of garbage. (Section deleted)

308.3.1 Garbage facilities. (Section deleted)

308.3.2 Containers. (Section deleted)

SECTION 309
PEST ELIMINATION

309.1 Infestation. This section shall apply to the extent that insect and rodent infestation adversely affects a structure. All structures shall be kept free from insect and rodent infestation. All structures in which insects or rodents are found shall be promptly exterminated by approved processes that will not be injurious to human health. After extermination, proper precautions shall be taken to prevent reinfestation.

309.2 Owner. The *owner* of any structure shall be responsible for pest elimination within the structure prior to renting or leasing the structure.

309.3 Single occupant. The *occupant* of a one-family dwelling or of a single-*tenant* nonresidential structure shall be responsible for pest elimination on the *premises*.

309.4 Multiple occupancy. The *owner* of a structure containing two or more *dwelling units*, a multiple *occupancy*, a *rooming house* or a nonresidential structure shall be responsible for pest elimination in the public or shared areas of the structure and *exterior property*. If *infestation* is caused by failure of an *occupant* to prevent such *infestation* in the area occupied, the *occupant* and *owner* shall be responsible for pest elimination.

309.5 Occupant. The *occupant* of any structure shall be responsible for the continued rodent and pest-free condition of the structure.

Exception: Where the *infestations* are caused by defects in the structure, the *owner* shall be responsible for pest elimination.

SECTION 310
LEAD-BASED PAINT

310.1 General. Interior and exterior painted surfaces of dwellings and child care facilities, including fences and outbuildings, that contain lead levels equal to or greater than 1.0 milligram per square centimeter or in excess of 0.50 percent lead by weight shall be maintained in a condition free from peeling, chipping and flaking paint or removed or covered in an approved manner. Any surface to be covered shall first be identified by an approved warning as to the lead content of such surface.

SECTION 311
ABOVEGROUND LIQUID
FERTILIZER STORAGE TANKS (ALFSTs)

311.1 General. ALFSTs shall be maintained in accordance with the requirements of Section 1701.16 of the VRC and the requirements of the VCC applicable to such ALFSTs when newly constructed and the requirements of the VRC when undergoing a change of occupancy to an ALFST and when repaired, altered or reconstructed, including the requirements for inspections and for a secondary containment system.

CHAPTER 4

LIGHT, VENTILATION AND OCCUPANCY LIMITATIONS

SECTION 401
GENERAL

401.1 Scope. The provisions of this chapter shall govern the minimum conditions and standards for light, *ventilation* and space for occupying a structure.

401.2 Responsibility. The *owner* of the structure shall provide and maintain light, *ventilation* and space conditions in compliance with these requirements. A person shall not occupy as *owner-occupant*, or permit another person to occupy, any *premises* that do not comply with the requirements of this chapter.

401.3 Alternative devices. In lieu of the means for natural light and *ventilation* herein prescribed, artificial light or mechanical *ventilation* complying with the *International Building Code* shall be permitted.

SECTION 402
LIGHT

402.1 Habitable spaces. Every *habitable space* shall have at least one window of *approved* size facing directly to the outdoors or to a court. The minimum total glazed area for every *habitable space* shall be 8 percent of the floor area of such room. Wherever walls or other portions of a structure face a window of any room and such obstructions are located less than 3 feet (914 mm) from the window and extend to a level above that of the ceiling of the room, such window shall not be deemed to face directly to the outdoors nor to a court and shall not be included as contributing to the required minimum total window area for the room.

Exception: Where natural light for rooms or spaces without exterior glazing areas is provided through an adjoining room, the unobstructed opening to the adjoining room shall be at least 8 percent of the floor area of the interior room or space, but a minimum of 25 square feet (2.33 m²). The exterior glazing area shall be based on the total floor area being served.

402.2 Common halls and stairways. Every common hall and stairway in residential occupancies, other than in one- and two-family dwellings, shall be lighted at all times with at least a 60-watt standard incandescent light bulb for each 200 square feet (19 m²) of floor area or equivalent illumination, provided that the spacing between lights shall not be greater than 30 feet (9144 mm). In other than residential occupancies, means of egress, including exterior means of egress, stairways shall be illuminated at all times the building space served by the means of egress is occupied with a minimum of 1 footcandle (11 lux) at floors, landings and treads.

402.3 Other spaces. All other spaces shall be provided with natural or artificial light sufficient to permit the maintenance of sanitary conditions, and the safe *occupancy* of the space and utilization of the appliances, equipment and fixtures.

SECTION 403
VENTILATION

403.1 Habitable spaces. Every *habitable space* shall have at least one openable window. The total openable area of the window in every room shall be equal to at least 45 percent of the minimum glazed area required in Section 402.1.

Exception: Where rooms and spaces without openings to the outdoors are ventilated through an adjoining room, the unobstructed opening to the adjoining room shall be at least 8 percent of the floor area of the interior room or space, but a minimum of 25 square feet (2.33 m²). The *ventilation* openings to the outdoors shall be based on a total floor area being ventilated.

403.2 Bathrooms and toilet rooms. Every *bathroom* and *toilet room* shall comply with the *ventilation* requirements for *habitable spaces* as required by Section 403.1, except that a window shall not be required in such spaces equipped with a mechanical *ventilation* system. Air exhausted by a mechanical *ventilation* system from a *bathroom* or *toilet room* shall discharge to the outdoors and shall not be recirculated.

403.3 Cooking facilities. Unless *approved* through the certificate of *occupancy*, cooking shall not be permitted in any *rooming unit* or dormitory unit, and a cooking facility or appliance shall not be permitted to be present in the *rooming unit* or dormitory unit.

Exceptions:

1. Where specifically *approved* in writing by the *code official*.

2. Devices such as coffee pots and microwave ovens shall not be considered cooking appliances.

403.4 Process ventilation. Where injurious, toxic, irritating or noxious fumes, gases, dusts or mists are generated, a local exhaust *ventilation* system shall be provided to remove the contaminating agent at the source. Air shall be exhausted to the exterior and not be recirculated to any space.

403.5 Clothes dryer exhaust. Clothes dryer exhaust systems shall be independent of all other systems and shall be exhausted outside the structure in accordance with the manufacturer's instructions.

Exception: Listed and *labeled* condensing (ductless) clothes dryers.

SECTION 404
OCCUPANCY LIMITATIONS

404.1 Privacy. *Dwelling units*, hotel units, *housekeeping units*, *rooming units* and dormitory units shall be arranged to provide privacy and be separate from other adjoining spaces.

404.2 Minimum room widths. A habitable room, other than a kitchen, shall be a minimum of 7 feet (2134 mm) in any plan dimension. Kitchens shall have a minimum clear passageway of 3 feet (914 mm) between counterfronts and appliances or counterfronts and walls.

404.3 Minimum ceiling heights. *Habitable spaces*, hallways, corridors, laundry areas, *bathrooms*, *toilet rooms* and habitable *basement* areas shall have a minimum clear ceiling height of 7 feet (2134 mm).

Exceptions:

1. In one- and two-family dwellings, beams or girders spaced a minimum of 4 feet (1219 mm) on center and projecting a maximum of 6 inches (152 mm) below the required ceiling height.

2. *Basement* rooms in one- and two-family dwellings occupied exclusively for laundry, study or recreation purposes, having a minimum ceiling height of 6 feet 8 inches (2033 mm) with a minimum clear height of 6 feet 4 inches (1932 mm) under beams, girders, ducts and similar obstructions.

3. Rooms occupied exclusively for sleeping, study or similar purposes and having a sloped ceiling over all or part of the room, with a minimum clear ceiling height of 7 feet (2134 mm) over a minimum of one-third of the required minimum floor area. In calculating the floor area of such rooms, only those portions of the floor area with a minimum clear ceiling height of 5 feet (1524 mm) shall be included.

404.4 Bedroom and living room requirements. Every *bedroom* and living room shall comply with the requirements of Sections 404.4.1 through 404.4.5.

404.4.1 Room area. Every living room shall contain at least 120 square feet (11.2 m²) and every bedroom shall contain a minimum of 70 square feet (6.5 m²) and every bedroom occupied by more than one person shall contain a minimum of 50 square feet (4.6 m²) of floor area for each occupant thereof.

404.4.2 Access from bedrooms. *Bedrooms* shall not constitute the only means of access to other *bedrooms* or *habitable spaces* and shall not serve as the only means of egress from other *habitable spaces*.

Exception: Units that contain fewer than two *bedrooms*.

404.4.3 Water closet accessibility. Every *bedroom* shall have access to at least one water closet and one lavatory without passing through another *bedroom*. Every *bedroom* in a *dwelling unit* shall have access to at least one water closet and lavatory located in the same story as the *bedroom* or an adjacent story.

404.4.4 Prohibited occupancy. Kitchens and nonhabitable spaces shall not be used for sleeping purposes.

404.4.5 Other requirements. *Bedrooms* shall comply with the applicable provisions of this code including, but not limited to, the light, *ventilation*, room area, ceiling height and room width requirements of this chapter; the plumbing facilities and water-heating facilities requirements of Chapter 5; the heating facilities and electrical

receptacle requirements of Chapter 6; and the smoke detector and emergency escape requirements of Chapter 7.

404.5 Overcrowding. Dwelling units shall not be occupied by more occupants than permitted by the minimum area requirements of Table 404.5.

TABLE 404.5
MINIMUM AREA REQUIREMENTS

SPACE	MINIMUM AREA IN SQUARE FEET		
	1-2 occupants	3-5 occupants	6 or more occupants
Living room[a, b]	120	120	150
Dining room[a, b]	No requirement	80	100
Bedrooms	Shall comply with Section 404.4.1		

For SI: 1 square foot = 0.093 m².

a. See Section 404.5.2 for combined living room/dining room spaces.

b. See Section 404.5.1 for limitations on determining the minimum occupancy area for sleeping purposes.

404.5.1 Sleeping area. The minimum occupancy area required by Table 404.5 shall not be included as a sleeping area in determining the minimum occupancy area for sleeping purposes. All sleeping areas shall comply with Section 404.4.

404.5.2 Combined spaces. Combined living room and dining room spaces shall comply with the requirements of Table 404.5 if the total area is equal to that required for separate rooms and if the space is located so as to function as a combination living room/dining room.

404.6 Efficiency unit. Nothing in this section shall prohibit an efficiency living unit from meeting the following requirements:

1. A unit occupied by not more than one occupant shall have a minimum clear floor area of 120 square feet (11.2 m²). A unit occupied by not more than two *occupants* shall have a minimum clear floor area of 220 square feet (20.4 m²). A unit occupied by three *occupants* shall have a minimum clear floor area of 320 square feet (29.7 m²). These required areas shall be exclusive of the areas required by Items 2 and 3.

2. The unit shall be provided with a kitchen sink, cooking appliance and refrigeration facilities, each having a minimum clear working space of 30 inches (762 mm) in front. Light and *ventilation* conforming to this code shall be provided.

3. The unit shall be provided with a separate *bathroom* containing a water closet, lavatory and bathtub or shower.

4. The maximum number of *occupants* shall be three.

404.7 Food preparation. All spaces to be occupied for food preparation purposes shall contain suitable space and equipment to store, prepare and serve foods in a sanitary manner. There shall be adequate facilities and services for the sanitary disposal of food wastes and refuse, including facilities for temporary storage.

CHAPTER 5

PLUMBING FACILITIES AND FIXTURE REQUIREMENTS

SECTION 501
GENERAL

501.1 Scope. The provisions of this chapter shall govern the minimum plumbing systems, facilities and plumbing fixtures to be provided.

501.2 Responsibility. The *owner* of the structure shall provide and maintain such plumbing facilities and plumbing fixtures in compliance with these requirements. A person shall not occupy as *owner-occupant* or permit another person to occupy any structure or *premises* which does not comply with the requirements of this chapter.

SECTION 502
REQUIRED FACILITIES

[P] 502.1 Dwelling units. Every *dwelling unit* shall contain its own bathtub or shower, lavatory, water closet and kitchen sink which shall be maintained in a sanitary, safe working condition. The lavatory shall be placed in the same room as the water closet or located in close proximity to the door leading directly into the room in which such water closet is located. A kitchen sink shall not be used as a substitute for the required lavatory.

[P] 502.2 Rooming houses. At least one water closet, lavatory and bathtub or shower shall be supplied for each four *rooming units*.

[P] 502.3 Hotels. Where private water closets, lavatories and baths are not provided, one water closet, one lavatory and one bathtub or shower having access from a public hallway shall be provided for each ten *occupants*.

[P] 502.4 Employees' facilities. A minimum of one water closet, one lavatory and one drinking facility shall be available to employees.

> **[P] 502.4.1 Drinking facilities.** Drinking facilities shall be a drinking fountain, water cooler, bottled water cooler or disposable cups next to a sink or water dispenser. Drinking facilities shall not be located in *toilet rooms* or *bathrooms*.

[P] 502.5 Public toilet facilities. Public toilet facilities shall be maintained in a safe sanitary and working condition in accordance with the *International Plumbing Code*. Except for periodic maintenance or cleaning, public access and use shall be provided to the toilet facilities at all times during *occupancy* of the *premises*.

SECTION 503
TOILET ROOMS

[P] 503.1 Privacy. *Toilet rooms* and *bathrooms* shall provide privacy and shall not constitute the only passageway to a hall or other space, or to the exterior. A door and interior locking device shall be provided for all common or shared *bathrooms* and *toilet rooms* in a multiple dwelling.

[P] 503.2 Location. *Toilet rooms* and *bathrooms* serving hotel units, *rooming units* or dormitory units or *housekeeping units*, shall have access by traversing a maximum of one flight of stairs and shall have access from a common hall or passageway.

[P] 503.3 Location of employee toilet facilities. Toilet facilities shall have access from within the employees' working area. The required toilet facilities shall be located a maximum of one story above or below the employees' working area and the path of travel to such facilities shall not exceed a distance of 500 feet (152 m). Employee facilities shall either be separate facilities or combined employee and public facilities.

> **Exception:** Facilities that are required for employees in storage structures or kiosks, which are located in adjacent structures under the same ownership, lease or control, shall not exceed a travel distance of 500 feet (152 m) from the employees' regular working area to the facilities.

[P] 503.4 Floor surface. In other than *dwelling units*, every *toilet room* floor shall be maintained to be a smooth, hard, nonabsorbent surface to permit such floor to be easily kept in a clean and sanitary condition.

SECTION 504
PLUMBING SYSTEMS AND FIXTURES

[P] 504.1 General. All plumbing fixtures shall be properly installed and maintained in working order, and shall be kept free from obstructions, leaks and defects and be capable of performing the function for which such plumbing fixtures are designed. All plumbing fixtures shall be maintained in a safe, sanitary and functional condition.

[P] 504.2 Fixture clearances. Plumbing fixtures shall have adequate clearances for usage and cleaning.

[P] 504.3 Plumbing system hazards. Where it is found that a plumbing system in a structure constitutes a hazard to the *occupants* or the structure by reason of inadequate service, inadequate venting, cross connection, backsiphonage, improper installation, *deterioration* or damage or for similar reasons, the *code official* shall require the defects to be corrected to eliminate the hazard.

SECTION 505
WATER SYSTEM

505.1 General. Every sink, lavatory, bathtub or shower, drinking fountain, water closet or other plumbing fixture shall be properly connected to either a public water system or to an *approved* private water system. All kitchen sinks, lavatories, laundry facilities, bathtubs and showers shall be supplied with hot or tempered and cold running water in accordance with the *International Plumbing Code*.

[P] 505.2 Contamination. The water supply shall be maintained free from contamination, and all water inlets for plumbing fixtures shall be located above the flood-level rim of the fixture. Shampoo basin faucets, janitor sink faucets and other hose bibs or faucets to which hoses are attached and left in place, shall be protected by an approved atmospheric-type vacuum breaker or an approved permanently attached hose connection vacuum breaker.

505.3 Supply. The water supply system shall be installed and maintained to provide a supply of water to plumbing fixtures, devices and appurtenances in sufficient volume and at pressures adequate to enable the fixtures to function properly, safely, and free from defects and leaks.

505.4 Water heating facilities. Water heating facilities shall be properly installed, maintained and capable of providing an adequate amount of water to be drawn at every required sink, lavatory, bathtub, shower and laundry facility at a minimum temperature of 110°F (43°C). A gas-burning water heater shall not be located in any *bathroom*, *toilet room*, *bedroom* or other occupied room normally kept closed, unless adequate combustion air is provided. An *approved* combination temperature and pressure-relief valve and relief valve discharge pipe shall be properly installed and maintained on water heaters.

505.5 Inspection and testing of backflow prevention assemblies. Inspection and testing shall comply with Sections 505.5.1 and 505.5.2.

505.5.1 Inspections. Inspections shall be made of all backflow prevention assemblies and air gaps to determine whether they are operable.

505.5.2 Testing. Reduced pressure principle backflow preventer assemblies, double check-valve assemblies, double-detector check valve assemblies and pressure vacuum breaker assemblies shall be tested at the time of installation, immediately after repairs or relocation and at least annually. The testing procedure shall be performed in accordance with one of the following standards: ASSE 5010-1013-1, Sections 1 and 2; ASSE 5010-1015-1, Sections 1 and 2; ASSE 5010-1015-2; ASSE 5010-1015-3, Sections 1 and 2; ASSE 5010-1015-4, Sections 1 and 2; ASSE 5010-1020-1, Sections 1 and 2; ASSE 5010-1047-1, Sections 1, 2, 3 and 4; ASSE 5010-1048-1, Sections 1, 2, 3 and 4; ASSE 5010-1048-2; ASSE 5010-1048-3, Sections 1, 2, 3 and 4; ASSE 5010-1048-4, Sections 1, 2, 3 and 4; or CAN/CSA B64.10.

SECTION 506
SANITARY DRAINAGE SYSTEM

[P] 506.1 General. All plumbing fixtures shall be properly connected to either a public sewer system or to an *approved* private sewage disposal system.

[P] 506.2 Maintenance. Every plumbing stack, vent, waste and sewer line shall function properly and be kept free from obstructions, leaks and defects.

[P] 506.3 Grease interceptors. Grease interceptors and automatic grease removal devices shall be maintained in accordance with this code and the manufacturer's installation instructions. Grease interceptors and automatic grease removal devices shall be regularly serviced and cleaned to prevent the discharge of oil, grease, and other substances harmful or hazardous to the building drainage system, the public sewer, the private sewage disposal system or the sewage treatment plant or processes. All records of maintenance, cleaning and repairs shall be available for inspection by the code official.

SECTION 507
STORM DRAINAGE

507.1 General. Drainage of roofs and paved areas, yards and courts, and other open areas on the premises shall be discharged in a manner to protect the buildings and structures from the accumulation of overland water runoff.

CHAPTER 6

MECHANICAL AND ELECTRICAL REQUIREMENTS

SECTION 601
GENERAL

601.1 Scope. The provisions of this chapter shall govern the minimum mechanical and electrical facilities and equipment to be provided.

601.2 Responsibility. The *owner* of the structure shall provide and maintain mechanical and electrical facilities and equipment in compliance with these requirements. A person shall not occupy as *owner-occupant* or permit another person to occupy any *premises* which does not comply with the requirements of this chapter.

SECTION 602
HEATING AND COOLING FACILITIES

602.1 Facilities required. Heating and cooling facilities shall be maintained and operated in structures as required by this section.

602.2 Heat supply. Every owner and operator of a Group R-2 apartment building or other residential dwelling who rents, leases or lets one or more dwelling unit, rooming unit, dormitory or guestroom on terms, either expressed or implied, to furnish heat to the occupants thereof shall supply heat during the period from October 15 to May 1 to maintain a temperature of not less than 65°F (18°C) in all habitable rooms, bathrooms, and toilet rooms. The code official may also consider modifications as provided in Section 104.5.2 when requested for unusual circumstances or may issue notice approving building owners to convert shared heating and cooling piping HVAC systems 14 calendar days before or after the established dates when extended periods of unusual temperatures merit modifying these dates.

> **Exception:** When the outdoor temperature is below the winter outdoor design temperature for the locality, maintenance of the minimum room temperature shall not be required provided that the heating system is operating at its full design capacity. The winter outdoor design temperature for the locality shall be as indicated in Appendix D of the *International Plumbing Code*.

602.2.1 Prohibited use. In dwelling units subject to Section 602.2, one or more unvented room heaters shall not be used as the sole source of comfort heat in a dwelling unit.

602.3 Occupiable work spaces. Indoor occupiable work spaces shall be supplied with heat during the period from October 1 to May 15 to maintain a temperature of not less than 65°F (18°C) during the period the spaces are occupied.

> **Exceptions:**
>
> 1. Processing, storage and operation areas that require cooling or special temperature conditions.
>
> 2. Areas in which persons are primarily engaged in vigorous physical activities.

602.4 Cooling supply. Every owner and operator of a Group R-2 apartment building who rents, leases or lets one or more dwelling units, rooming units or guestrooms on terms, either expressed or implied, to furnish cooling to the occupants thereof shall supply cooling during the period from May 15 to October 1 to maintain a temperature of not more than 80°F (27°C) in all habitable rooms. The code official may also consider modifications as provided in Section 104.5.2 when requested for unusual circumstances or may issue notice approving building owners to convert shared heating and cooling piping HVAC systems 14 calendar days before or after the established dates when extended periods of unusual temperatures merit modifying these dates.

> **Exception:** When the outdoor temperature is higher than the summer design temperature for the locality, maintenance of the room temperature shall not be required provided that the cooling system is operating at its full design capacity. The summer outdoor design temperature for the locality shall be as indicated in the *International Energy Conservation Code*.

602.5 Room temperature measurement. The required room temperatures shall be measured 3 feet (914 mm) above the floor near the center of the room and 2 feet (610 mm) inward from the center of each exterior wall.

SECTION 603
MECHANICAL EQUIPMENT

603.1 Mechanical appliances. All mechanical appliances, fireplaces, solid fuel-burning appliances, cooking appliances and water heating appliances shall be properly installed and maintained in a safe working condition, and shall be capable of performing the intended function.

603.2 Removal of combustion products. All fuel-burning equipment and appliances shall be connected to an *approved* chimney or vent.

> **Exception:** Fuel-burning equipment and appliances which are *labeled* for unvented operation.

603.3 Clearances. All required clearances to combustible materials shall be maintained.

603.4 Safety controls. All safety controls for fuel-burning equipment shall be maintained in effective operation.

603.5 Combustion air. A supply of air for complete combustion of the fuel and for *ventilation* of the space containing the fuel-burning equipment shall be provided for the fuel-burning equipment.

603.6 Energy conservation devices. Devices intended to reduce fuel consumption by attachment to a fuel-burning appliance, to the fuel supply line thereto, or to the vent outlet or vent piping therefrom, shall not be installed unless *labeled* for such purpose and the installation is specifically *approved*.

SECTION 604
ELECTRICAL FACILITIES

604.1 Facilities required. Every occupied building shall be provided with an electrical system in compliance with the requirements of this section and Section 605.

604.2 Service. The size and usage of appliances and equipment shall serve as a basis for determining the need for additional facilities in accordance with NFPA 70. *Dwelling units* shall be served by a three-wire, 120/240 volt, single-phase electrical service having a minimum rating of 60 amperes.

604.3 Electrical system hazards. Where it is found that the electrical system in a structure constitutes a hazard to the *occupants* or the structure by reason of inadequate service, improper fusing, insufficient receptacle and lighting outlets, improper wiring or installation, *deterioration* or damage, or for similar reasons, the *code official* shall require the defects to be corrected to eliminate the hazard.

604.3.1 Abatement of electrical hazards associated with water exposure. The provisions of this section shall govern the repair and replacement of electrical systems and equipment that have been exposed to water.

604.3.1.1 Electrical equipment. Electrical distribution equipment, motor circuits, power equipment, transformers, wire, cable, flexible cords, wiring devices, ground fault circuit interrupters, surge protectors, molded case circuit breakers, low-voltage fuses, luminaires, ballasts, motors and electronic control, signaling and communication equipment that have been exposed to water shall be replaced in accordance with the provisions of the *International Building Code.*

Exception: The following equipment shall be allowed to be repaired or reused where an inspection report from the equipment manufacturer, an approved representative of the equipment manufacturer, a third party licensed or certified electrician, or an electrical engineer indicates that the exposed equipment has not sustained damage that requires replacement:

1. Enclosed switches, rated 600 volts or less;
2. Busway, rated 600 volts or less;
3. Panelboards, rated 600 volts or less;
4. Switchboards, rated 600 volts or less;
5. Fire pump controllers, rated 600 volts or less;
6. Manual and magnetic motor controllers;
7. Motor control centers;
8. Alternating current high-voltage circuit breakers;
9. Low-voltage power circuit breakers;
10. Protective relays, meters and current transformers;
11. Low- and medium-voltage switchgear;
12. Liquid-filled transformers;
13. Cast-resin transformers;
14. Wire or cable that is suitable for wet locations and whose ends have not been exposed to water;
15. Wire or cable, not containing fillers, that is suitable for wet locations and whose ends have not been exposed to water;
16. Luminaires that are listed as submersible;
17. Motors;
18. Electronic control, signaling and communication equipment.

604.3.2 Abatement of electrical hazards associated with fire exposure. The provisions of this section shall govern the repair and replacement of electrical systems and equipment that have been exposed to fire.

604.3.2.1 Electrical equipment. Electrical switches, receptacles and fixtures, including furnace, water heating, security system and power distribution circuits, that have been exposed to fire, shall be replaced in accordance with the provisions of the *International Building Code.*

Exception: Electrical switches, receptacles and fixtures that shall be allowed to be repaired where an inspection report from the equipment manufacturer or *approved* manufacturer's representative indicates that the equipment has not sustained damage that requires replacement.

SECTION 605
ELECTRICAL EQUIPMENT

605.1 Installation. All electrical equipment, wiring and appliances shall be properly installed and maintained in a safe and *approved* manner.

605.2 Receptacles. Every *habitable space* in a dwelling shall contain at least two separate and remote receptacle outlets. Every laundry area shall contain at least one grounding-type receptacle or a receptacle with a ground fault circuit interrupter. Every *bathroom* shall contain at least one receptacle. Any new *bathroom* receptacle outlet shall have ground fault circuit interrupter protection. All receptacle outlets shall have the appropriate faceplate cover for the location.

605.3 Luminaires. Every public hall, interior stairway, *toilet room*, kitchen, *bathroom*, laundry room, boiler room and furnace room shall contain at least one electric luminaire. Pool and spa luminaries over 15 V shall have ground fault circuit interrupter protection.

605.4 Wiring. Flexible cords shall not be used for permanent wiring, or for running through doors, windows, or cabinets, or concealed within walls, floors, or ceilings.

SECTION 606
ELEVATORS, ESCALATORS AND DUMBWAITERS

606.1 General. Elevators, dumbwaiters and escalators shall be maintained in compliance with ASME A17.1. The most current certificate of inspection shall be on display at all times within the elevator or attached to the escalator or dumbwaiter, be available for public inspection in the office of the building operator or be posted in a publicly conspicuous location approved by the code official. An annual periodic inspection and test is required of elevators and escalators. A locality shall be permitted to require a six-month periodic inspection and test. All periodic inspections shall be performed in accordance with Section 8.11 of ASME A17.1. The code official may also provide for such inspection by an approved agency or through agreement with other local certified elevator inspectors. An approved agency includes any individual, partnership or corporation who has met the certification requirements established by the Virginia Certification Standards.

606.2 Elevators. In buildings equipped with passenger elevators, at least one elevator shall be maintained in operation at all times when the building is occupied.

> **Exception:** Buildings equipped with only one elevator shall be permitted to have the elevator temporarily out of service for testing or servicing.

SECTION 607
DUCT SYSTEMS

607.1 General. Duct systems shall be maintained free of obstructions and shall be capable of performing the required function.

CHAPTER 7

FIRE SAFETY REQUIREMENTS

SECTION 701
GENERAL

701.1 Scope. The provisions of this chapter shall govern the minimum conditions and standards for fire safety relating to structures and exterior *premises*, including fire safety facilities and equipment to be provided.

701.2 Responsibility. The *owner* of the *premises* shall provide and maintain such fire safety facilities and equipment in compliance with these requirements. A person shall not occupy as *owner-occupant* or permit another person to occupy any *premises* that do not comply with the requirements of this chapter.

SECTION 702
MEANS OF EGRESS

[F] 702.1 General. A safe, continuous and unobstructed path of travel shall be provided from any point in a building or structure to the *public way*. Means of egress shall comply with the *International Fire Code*.

[F] 702.2 Aisles. The required width of aisles in accordance with the *International Fire Code* shall be unobstructed.

[F] 702.3 Locked doors. All means of egress doors shall be readily openable from the side from which egress is to be made without the need for keys, special knowledge or effort, except where the door hardware conforms to that permitted by the *International Building Code*.

[F] 702.4 Emergency escape openings. Required emergency escape openings shall be maintained in accordance with the code in effect at the time of construction, and the following. Required emergency escape and rescue openings shall be operational from the inside of the room without the use of keys or tools. Bars, grilles, grates or similar devices are permitted to be placed over emergency escape and rescue openings provided the minimum net clear opening size complies with the code that was in effect at the time of construction and such devices shall be releasable or removable from the inside without the use of a key, tool or force greater than that which is required for normal operation of the escape and rescue opening.

SECTION 703
FIRE-RESISTANCE RATINGS

[F] 703.1 Fire-resistance-rated assemblies. The required fire-resistance rating of fire-resistance-rated walls, fire stops, shaft enclosures, partitions and floors shall be maintained.

[F] 703.2 Opening protectives. Required opening protectives shall be maintained in an operative condition. All fire and smokestop doors shall be maintained in operable condi-

tion. Fire doors and smoke barrier doors shall not be blocked or obstructed or otherwise made inoperable.

SECTION 704
FIRE PROTECTION SYSTEMS

[F] 704.1 General. All systems, devices and equipment to detect a fire, actuate an alarm, or suppress or control a fire or any combination thereof shall be maintained in an operable condition at all times in accordance with the *International Fire Code*.

[F] 704.1.1 Automatic sprinkler systems. Inspection, testing and maintenance of automatic sprinkler systems shall be in accordance with NFPA 25.

[F] 704.2 Smoke alarms. Single- or multiple-station smoke alarms shall be installed and maintained in Group R or I-1 occupancies, regardless of *occupant* load at all of the following locations:

1. On the ceiling or wall outside of each separate sleeping area in the immediate vicinity of *bedrooms*.

2. In each room used for sleeping purposes.

3. In each story within a *dwelling unit*, including *basements* and cellars but not including crawl spaces and uninhabitable attics. In dwellings or *dwelling units* with split levels and without an intervening door between the adjacent levels, a smoke alarm installed on the upper level shall suffice for the adjacent lower level provided that the lower level is less than one full story below the upper level.

[F] 704.3 Power source. In Group R or I-1 occupancies, single-station smoke alarms shall receive their primary power from the building wiring provided that such wiring is served from a commercial source and shall be equipped with a battery backup. Smoke alarms shall emit a signal when the batteries are low. Wiring shall be permanent and without a disconnecting switch other than as required for overcurrent protection.

Exception: Smoke alarms are permitted to be solely battery operated in buildings where no construction is taking place, buildings that are not served from a commercial power source and in existing areas of buildings undergoing alterations or repairs that do not result in the removal of interior wall or ceiling finishes exposing the structure, unless there is an attic, crawl space or basement available which could provide access for building wiring without the removal of interior finishes.

[F] 704.4 Interconnection. Where more than one smoke alarm is required to be installed within an individual *dwelling unit* in Group R or I-1 occupancies, the smoke alarms shall be interconnected in such a manner that the activation of one alarm will activate all of the alarms in the individual unit. Physical interconnection of smoke alarms shall not be required where listed wireless alarms are installed and all alarms sound upon activation of one alarm. The alarm shall be clearly audible in all *bedrooms* over background noise levels with all intervening doors closed.

Exceptions:

1. Interconnection is not required in buildings which are not undergoing alterations, repairs or construction of any kind.

2. Smoke alarms in existing areas are not required to be interconnected where alterations or repairs do not result in the removal of interior wall or ceiling finishes exposing the structure, unless there is an attic, crawl space or *basement* available which could provide access for interconnection without the removal of interior finishes.

CHAPTER 8

REFERENCED STANDARDS

This chapter lists the standards that are referenced in various sections of this document. The standards are listed herein by the promulgating agency of the standard, the standard identification, the effective date and title and the section or sections of this document that reference the standard. The application of the referenced standards shall be as specified in Section 102.7.

ASME

American Society of Mechanical Engineers
Three Park Avenue
New York, NY 10016-5990

Standard reference number	Title	Referenced in code section number
A17.1/CSA B44—2007	Safety Code for Elevators and Escalators 606.1	

ASTM

ASTM International
100 Barr Harbor Drive
West Conshohocken, PA 19428-2959

Standard reference number	Title	Referenced in code section number
F 1346—91 (2003)	Performance Specifications for Safety Covers and Labeling Requirements for All Covers for Swimming Pools, Spas and Hot Tubs 303.2	

ICC

International Code Council
500 New Jersey Avenue, NW
6th Floor
Washington, DC 20001

Standard reference number	Title	Referenced in code section number
IBC—12	International Building Code® 201.3, 401.3, 702.3	
IEBC—12	International Existing Building Code® 305.1.1, 306.1.1	
IFC—12	International Fire Code® 201.3, 604.3.1.1, 604.3.2.1, 702.1, 702.2, 704.1, 704.2	
IMC—12	International Mechanical Code® 201.3	
IPC—12	International Plumbing Code® 201.3, 505.1, 602.2, 602.3	
IRC—12	International Residential Code® 201.3	
IZC—12	International Zoning Code® 201.3	

NFPA

National Fire Protection Association
1 Batterymarch Park
Quincy, MA 02269

Standard reference number	Title	Referenced in code section number
25—11	Inspection, Testing and Maintenance of Water-Based Fire Protection Systems 704.1.1	
70—11	National Electrical Code 201.3, 604.2	

APPENDIX A

BOARDING STANDARD

DHCD Note: This appendix is informative and is not an official part of the Virginia Maintenance Code.

A101
GENERAL

A101.1 General. All windows and doors shall be boarded in an *approved* manner to prevent entry by unauthorized persons and shall be painted to correspond to the color of the existing structure.

A102
MATERIALS

A102.1 Boarding sheet material. Boarding sheet material shall be minimum $^1/_2$-inch (12.7 mm) thick wood structural panels complying with the *International Building Code*.

A102.2 Boarding framing material. Boarding framing material shall be minimum nominal 2-inch by 4-inch (51 mm by 102 mm) solid sawn lumber complying with the *International Building Code*.

A102.3 Boarding fasteners. Boarding fasteners shall be minimum $^3/_8$-inch (9.5 mm) diameter carriage bolts of such a length as required to penetrate the assembly and as required to adequately attach the washers and nuts. Washers and nuts shall comply with the *International Building Code*.

A103
INSTALLATION

A103.1 Boarding installation. The boarding installation shall be in accordance with Figures A103.1(1) and A103.1(2) and Sections A103.2 through A103.5.

A103.2 Boarding sheet material. The boarding sheet material shall be cut to fit the door or window opening neatly or shall be cut to provide an equal overlap at the perimeter of the door or window.

A103.3 Windows. The window shall be opened to allow the carriage bolt to pass through or the window sash shall be removed and stored. The 2-inch by 4-inch (51 mm by 102 mm) strong back framing material shall be cut minimum 2 inches (51 mm) wider than the window opening and shall be placed on the inside of the window opening 6 inches minimum above the bottom and below the top of the window opening. The framing and boarding shall be predrilled. The assembly shall be aligned and the bolts, washers and nuts shall be installed and secured.

A103.4 Door walls. The door opening shall be framed with minimum 2-inch by 4-inch (51 mm by 102 mm) framing material secured at the entire perimeter and vertical members at a maximum of 24 inches (610 mm) on center. Blocking shall also be secured at a maximum of 48 inches (1219 mm) on center vertically. Boarding sheet material shall be secured with screws and nails alternating every 6 inches (152 mm) on center.

A103.5 Doors. Doors shall be secured by the same method as for windows or door openings. One door to the structure shall be available for authorized entry and shall be secured and locked in an *approved* manner.

A104
REFERENCED STANDARDS

IBC—12   International Building Code   A102.1, A102.2, A102.3

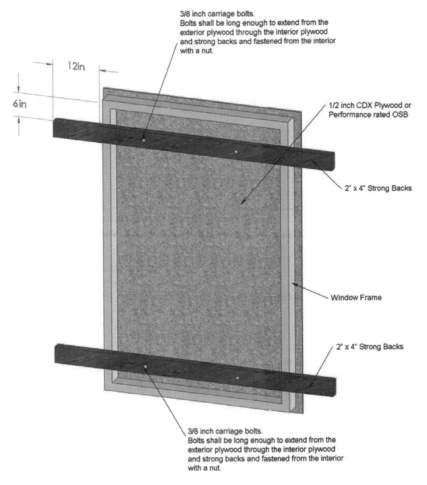

3/8 inch carriage bolts.
Bolts shall be long enough to extend from the
exterior plywood through the interior plywood
and strong backs and fastened from the interior
with a nut.

12in

6 in

1/2 inch CDX Plywood or
Performance rated OSB

2" x 4" Strong Backs

Window Frame

2" x 4" Strong Backs

3/8 inch carriage bolts.
Bolts shall be long enough to extend from the
exterior plywood through the interior plywood
and strong backs and fastened from the interior
with a nut.

FIGURE A103.1(1)
BOARDING OF DOOR OR WINDOW

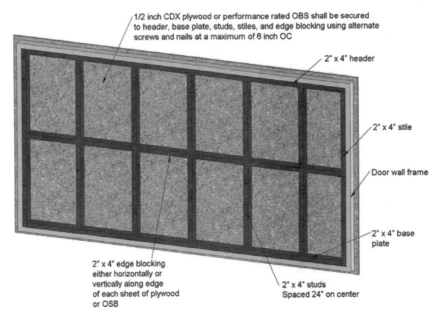

1/2 inch CDX plywood or performance rated OBS shall be secured
to header, base plate, studs, stiles, and edge blocking using alternate
screws and nails at a maximum of 6 inch OC

2" x 4" header

2" x 4" stile

Door wall frame

2" x 4" base
plate

2" x 4" edge blocking
either horizontally or
vertically along edge
of each sheet of plywood
or OSB

2" x 4" studs
Spaced 24" on center

FIGURE A103.1(2)
BOARDING OF DOOR WALL

INDEX